This JoJo & G...

storybook be...

First published in Great Britain in 2021 by Pat-a-Cake
Pat-a-Cake is a registered trademark of Hodder & Stoughton Limited
This book copyright © BBC 2021
JoJo & Gran Gran and the CBeebies logo are trademarks of the British Broadcasting Corporation and are used under licence
Based on original characters by Laura Henry-Allain MBE
Additional images © Shutterstock
ISBN 978 1 52638 354 9
1 3 5 7 9 10 8 6 4 2
Pat-a-Cake, an imprint of Hachette Children's Group,
Part of Hodder & Stoughton Limited
Carmelite House, 50 Victoria Embankment, London EC4Y 0DZ
An Hachette UK Company
EU address: 8 Castlecourt, Castleknock, Dublin 15, Ireland
www.hachette.co.uk · www.hachettechildrens.co.uk
Printed and bound in China
A CIP catalogue record for this book is available from the British Library

JoJo & GranGran

COOK TOGETHER

pat
a
cake

Picture Glossary

Here are some words from JoJo and Gran Gran's special cooking day.

JoJo

Gran Gran

Great Gran Gran

Cynthia

trowel

callaloo

clippers

recipe book

vegetables

soup

It was an autumn day. The leaves were changing colour and falling from the trees, and JoJo and Gran Gran were in the kitchen looking for a recipe to make with callaloo.

"Here it is," said Gran Gran, pulling a recipe book from the shelf.

"Saint Lucian Callaloo Soup," she read out, showing JoJo. "It's one of my favourites. Great Gran Gran used to make it to …

warm
my
tummy!"

She laughed and tickled JoJo to make her giggle.

Just then, Gran Gran's tablet started to ring. Gran Gran pressed green to answer and Great Gran Gran appeared on the screen.

"JoJo, my little sunshine!" she said. "How lovely to see you!"

"Hello, Great Gran Gran!" JoJo grinned. "We're making Ca … Cal …"
She couldn't remember the name of the special recipe.

"Callaloo Soup," finished Gran Gran, with a smile.

"Oh ho, delicious!" said Great Gran Gran. "One of my favourite dishes."

"That's what Gran Gran said," replied JoJo.

"Of course. I taught Gran Gran how to cook it … even though mine is tastier," Great Gran Gran added with a chuckle.

"I heard that, Mama!" said Gran Gran.

"You were meant to!" Great Gran Gran giggled.

"Has Gran Gran told you about the special ingredient yet, JoJo?" asked Great Gran Gran.

"Not yet," said Gran Gran. "We have the callaloo already but we still have some vegetables to buy."

"Say no more, I'll call you later." Great Gran Gran hung up, and JoJo and Gran Gran checked the recipe to see what they needed from Jared's shop.

Then JoJo and Gran Gran put on their coats and headed off.

Outside, Gran Gran's neighbour
Cynthia came by holding a bag and a spade.
"Hello there JoJo, Gran Gran. I'm just off to my allotment. It's where
I grow my vegetables."
"You GROW your vegetables?" asked JoJo. "We're going to Jared's shop
to BUY our vegetables."

"Well," explained Gran Gran, "before those vegetables arrive in Jared's shop, they have to be grown somewhere."

"And harvested," added Cynthia.

"What's *harvested*?" asked JoJo.

"When a vegetable has grown and is ready to eat, it has to be dug up or picked or clipped … it's called harvesting."

"Ooh!" JoJo said. She liked the sound of harvesting.

JoJo and Gran Gran arrived at Jared's shop.

Jared was there but the shutter was closed and there wasn't
a vegetable to be seen. Puddles of water covered the ground outside.

"Hey Gran Gran, JoJo!" Jared waved.

"Hi, Jared. Are you closed?" asked Gran Gran.

"Sorry," said Jared, looking sad. "I had to close the shop early today. A pipe's burst … there's water everywhere!"

"Oh no," said JoJo. "Where will we get our vegetables from?"

"Mmm," thought Gran Gran. "I think it's time for a Gran Gran plan!"

Gran Gran took JoJo to Cynthia's allotment.

Cynthia was busy harvesting her vegetables.

"Hello again JoJo, Gran Gran," she said.

"Can we help you harvest your vegetables, please?" asked JoJo, excitedly.

"Of course!" replied Cynthia.

"You'll need a trowel …

"And a sack …

"Perfect! Now, what vegetables do you need?"

"We're making Callaloo Soup," said JoJo. "We've already got

the callaloo, but we still need …"

She thought very hard.

Gran Gran helped. "Sweet potatoes, onions and a sprig of …"

"Thyme!" remembered JoJo.

"You're in luck. I've grown all three," said Cynthia.

JoJo smiled, looking at the pictures in the recipe book. She looked at the allotment, then back at the recipe book. Her smile faded a little as something seemed to be wrong.

"But ..." she said, "where are they?" JoJo couldn't see any of the vegetables pictured in her recipe book.

"Ah," said Cynthia, "we haven't harvested them yet!"

"We harvest vegetables by digging

and picking

and clipping!"

So JoJo and Gran Gran got to work **digging** ...

and picking ...

and clipping ...

until their sacks were bursting with vegetables for the special recipe.

"Harvesting vegetables is hard work!" said JoJo.

"It sure is," replied Cynthia. "But it's worth it when you're using the vegetables to make soup."

"Soup that warms … your … tummy!" added Gran Gran, tickling JoJo again. "Would you like to come for a bowl later, Cynthia? Our way of saying thank you."

On the way home they passed Jared's shop. It was open again.
The burst pipe had been fixed.

"JoJo! Did you manage to get your vegetables?" called Jared.

"We harvested some at Cynthia's allotment," JoJo told him.

"And now we're all having
Callaloo Soup!" added Gran Gran.
"Come too! And bring some flour - you can
make the dumplings!"

Back at Gran Gran's house, everyone tucked into delicious bowls of Callaloo Soup. There were lots of slurps and yummy noises.

Gran Gran's tablet started to ring.
It was Great Gran Gran again.

"JoJo!" she said. "My little sunshine! Did you make the Callaloo Soup?"

"Yes," said JoJo. "And we harvested our own vegetables, too."
She showed Great Gran Gran the soup and all of the vegetables
they had harvested. "We harvested sweet potato, onions and a sprig of
thyme." JoJo pointed at each vegetable with her spoon.

"Delicious!"

said Great Gran Gran.

"And did you add the special ingredient?" asked Great Gran Gran.

JoJo looked disappointed.
"Oh no! Gran Gran, we forgot the special ingredient," she said.

"But we didn't, JoJo," replied Gran Gran. "The special ingredient is ...

love!"

After Cynthia and Jared had gone home,

JoJo and Gran Gran sat on the sofa.

"I liked harvesting our own vegetables," said JoJo.

"Me too!" said Gran Gran.

"Next time we cook together, can we harvest more vegetables?"

"We'll have to grow them first!" chuckled Gran Gran.

"I love you, Gran Gran."

"Ahh, I love you too, JoJo."

Callaloo Soup Recipe

You can make your very own Callaloo Soup at home with this recipe!
Make sure you ask a grown-up to help.

Ingredients for 4 servings:

450g callaloo or spinach leaves
(fresh or tinned)

1.5 litres chicken or vegetable stock

1 onion, chopped

250g salt beef, fat removed
and diced (leave this out for a
vegetarian version)

2 medium potatoes, white or sweet,
diced

3 shallots, finely diced

100g okra, sliced

1 chilli (optional)

1 sprig fresh thyme or ½ teaspoon
of dried thyme

½ teaspoon ground black pepper

Salt to taste (optional)

Method:

1. Remove the thick stems of the callaloo, then chop the leaves roughly. If using canned callaloo, drain the brine. Put the leaves into a large saucepan.

2. Add the stock, onion, beef, black pepper, shallots, potatoes, thyme and chilli. Cover and simmer for 30-35 minutes (until meat is tender, if using).

3. Add the okra and cook for a further 10 minutes.

4. Remove the chilli, then puree the soup in a blender or food processor - or leave it chunky like JoJo and Gran Gran did!

5. Return to the pan to reheat. Adjust seasonings and serve.

Warning: requires adult supervision